The

Written by Rozanne Lanczak Williams
Created by Sue Lewis
Illustrated by Patty Briles

Creative Teaching Press

The Blob
© 2002 Creative Teaching Press, Inc.
Written by Rozanne Lanczak Williams
Illustrated by Patty Briles
Project Manager: Sue Lewis
Project Director: Carolea Williams

Published in the United States of America by:
Creative Teaching Press, Inc.
P.O. Box 2723
Huntington Beach, CA 92647-0723

ISBN-13: 978-1-57471-885-0
CTP 3251

Click, clack! The Blob goes
click clack down the track.

2

Slip, slide! Slip, slide!

The Blob goes sliding
on a fun sled ride!

Splish, splash! Glug, glug!

The Blob jumped in
and ate a bug.

Flip, flop! Flip, fly!

The Blob goes flying...

in the sky!

Create your own book!

Cut out several Blobs from blue construction paper. Attach the Blobs to the pages of a blank book. Using sets of rhyming words, write and illustrate a poem about your Blob.

Words in *The Blob*

Blends: *bl, cl, sl, gl, fl, spl*		High-Frequency Words	Other
slip	flop	the	down
slide	fly	on	track
sliding	flying	a	ride
sled	Blob	in	jumped
click		and	ate
clack			bug
splish			sky
splash			goes
glug			fun
flip			